Dedicated to my love,
my reason...R.G.A.
Mommy loves you!

This is my hero,
just daddy to me.
He has many names,
most call him L.T.

His boots are worn thin,
His hat a sweaty mess,
My hero's suit of armor,
Displays the finest code of dress.

Daddy trains with S.W.A.T.,
The toughest of them all.

They take on any danger,
They must answer every call.

Daddy will miss baseball playoffs,
I'm a big boy, That is okay.
He is saving lives again,
And they will live another day.

Meet daddy's partner,
most call him K9-3,
My puppy and best friend,
He is just Niko to me.

Niko is on duty with daddy,
I'm a big boy that's ok,
He is saving lives again,
And they will live another day.

A snuggler off duty,
we play all the while,
Bad guys beware of this
teeth filled smile.

Mommy is my hero,
Beautifully strong she holds a shield.
She saves the city from danger,
To villains she will not yield.

My hero defends all people,
To her values she remains true.
Always proud to be her daughter,
This family respects the blue.

Today is my birthday,
Finally I am eight!
The party is starting,
My hero will be late.

Daddy will miss the party,
I'm a big boy, That is ok,
He is saving lives again,
And they will live another day.

Today is my dance recital,
We practiced every week.
My hero was called to duty,
To protect the scared and meek.

Mommy wont see me dance today,
I'm a big girl, That is ok.
She is saving lives again,
And they will live another day.

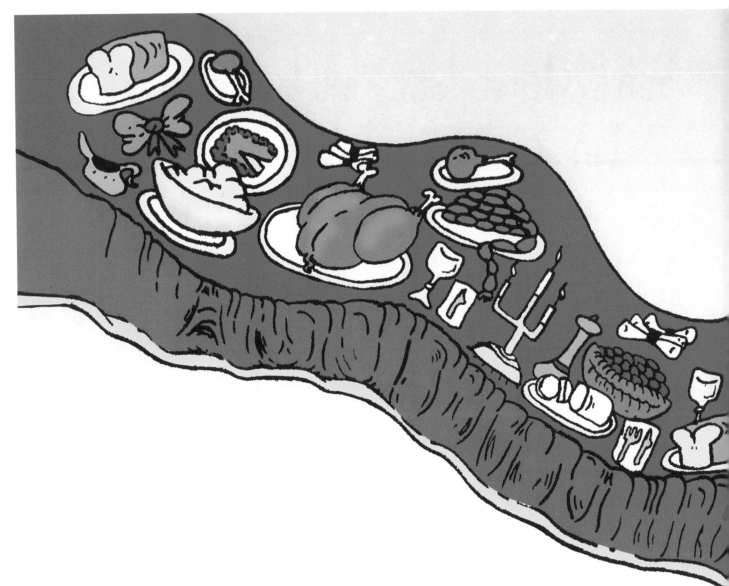

The holidays are here,
The food smells so delicious.
Not one turkey but five,
Perhaps a million side dishes!

My hero is on duty this magical night,
Side by side with our huge (Leo) family
Police prayers said by candlelight.

Daddy won't be there,
I'm a big boy, that is ok.
He is saving lives again,
And they will live another day.

It is time for snuggles,
Time for wishes to come true.
Time for big boy prayers,
And storytime tales of what's new.

Mommy won't be there,
I'm a big girl, That is ok.
She is saving lives again,
And they will live another day.

So say thank you to your hero,
I thank the lord each day for mine.
Cherish each moment you have,
Every second is precious time.

It is morning now,
Shhhh do not make a peep!
Daddy is finally home,
He just went to sleep.

My hero sleeps through the day
And that is alright.
Mommy made sure we were safe,
While we dreamt through the night.

THE END

CPSIA information can be obtained
at www.ICGtesting.com
Printed in the USA
LVHW070428040920
665076LV00012B/505